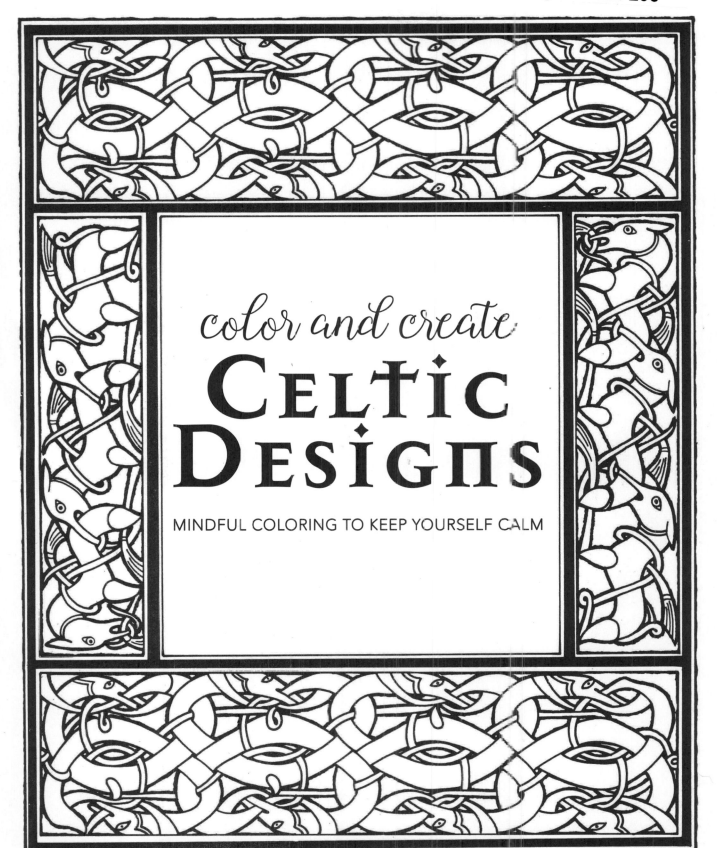

color and create

CELTIC
DESIGNS

MINDFUL COLORING TO KEEP YOURSELF CALM

METRO BOOKS
New York

An imprint of Sterling Publishing
1166 Avenue of the Americas
17th Floor
New York, NY 10036

ISBN 978-1-4351-6200-6

For information about custom editions, special sales, and premium and corporate purchases, please contact
Sterling Special Sales at 800-805-5489
or specialsales@sterlingpublishing.com.

Acknowledgements:
Publisher: Samantha Warrington
Design: Wide Open Studios
Art Director: Miranda Snow
Editor: Phoebe Morgan
With special thanks to Maire B Uí Mhathúna and Domhnall O'Mahony

Manufactured in China

2 4 6 8 10 9 7 5 3 1

www.sterlingpublishing.com

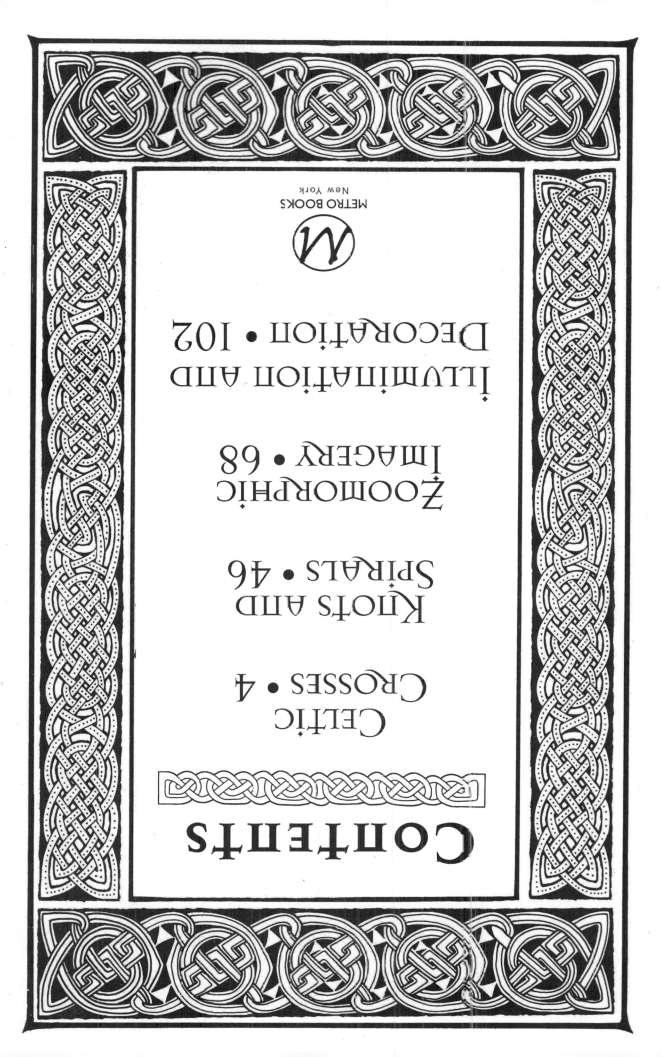

Contents

Ⓜ
METRO BOOKS
New York

CELTIC CROSSES

RECOGNISED THE WORLD OVER, the Celtic Cross originated in Gaelic Ireland and combines a traditional cross with a circle intersecting its stem and arms. Theories and myths abound about the meaning of the circle, one being that it represents the Celtic Sun God 'Taranis' or the Roman Sun God 'Invictus', another that the ring was added to a conventional cross by St. Patrick in an attempt to unite Christian and Pagan faiths. But many believe that the circle was added to the cross structure by stonemasons simply for strength. However it came to be, this powerful symbol has endured for thousands of years.

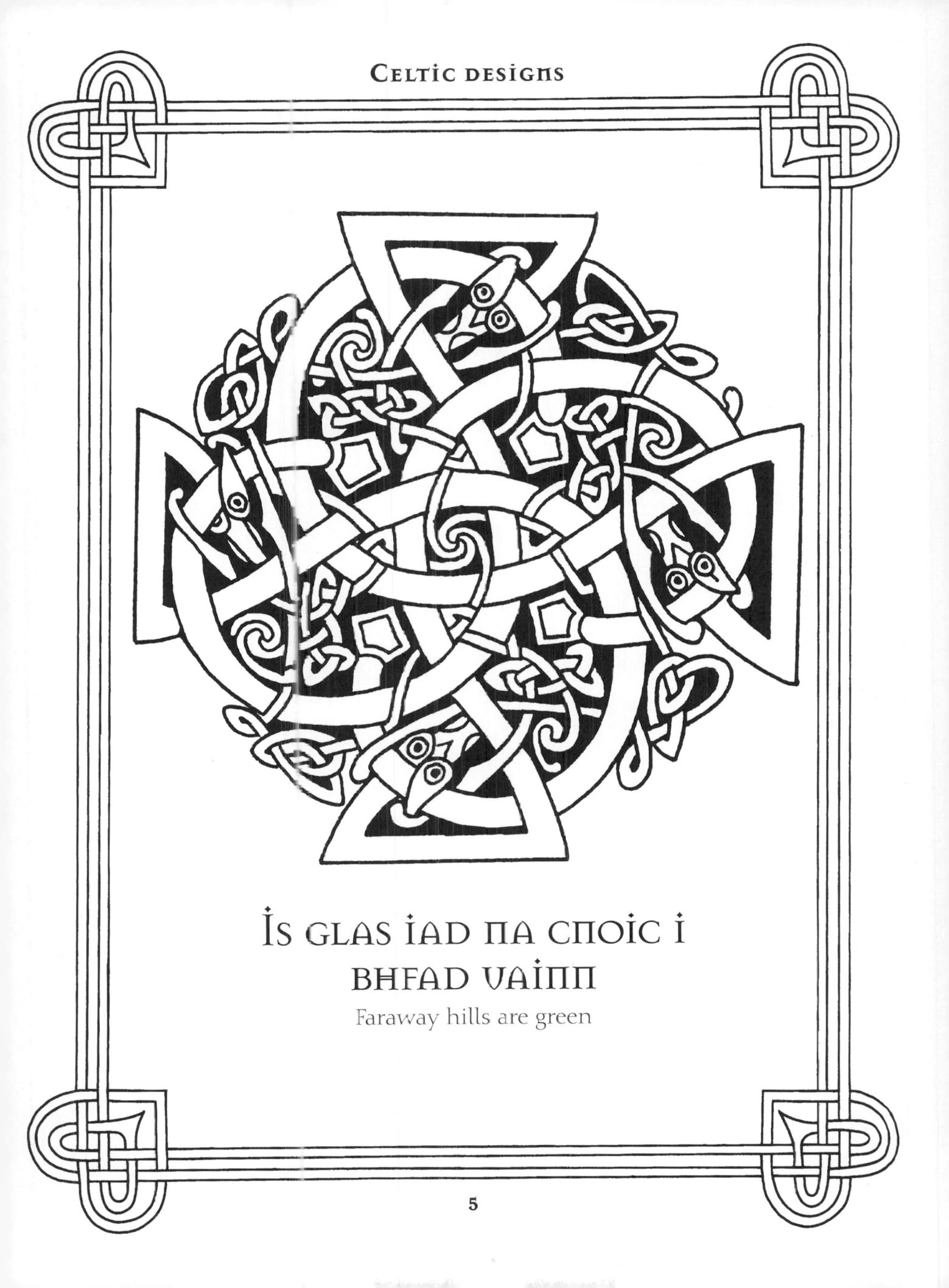

Is glas iad na cnoic i bhfad uainn

Faraway hills are green

BEÌRÌDH AM BEAG TRÌC AÌR A MHÒR AÌNMÌG

Little and often is better than all at once

CÉAD MÍLE FÁILTE

A hundred thousand welcomes

DÉANAII GRÁ AR FUD AN DOMHAIN DUL BHABÍTA

Love makes the world go round

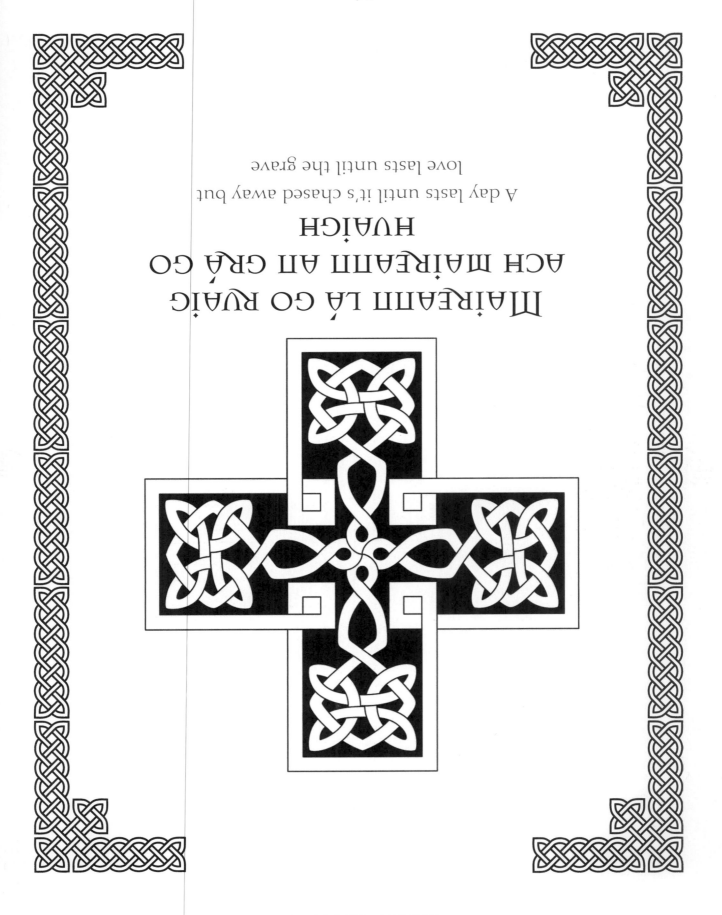

MAIREANN LÁ GO RUAIG ACH MAIREANN AN GRÁ GO HUAIGH

A day lasts until it's chased away but
love lasts until the grave

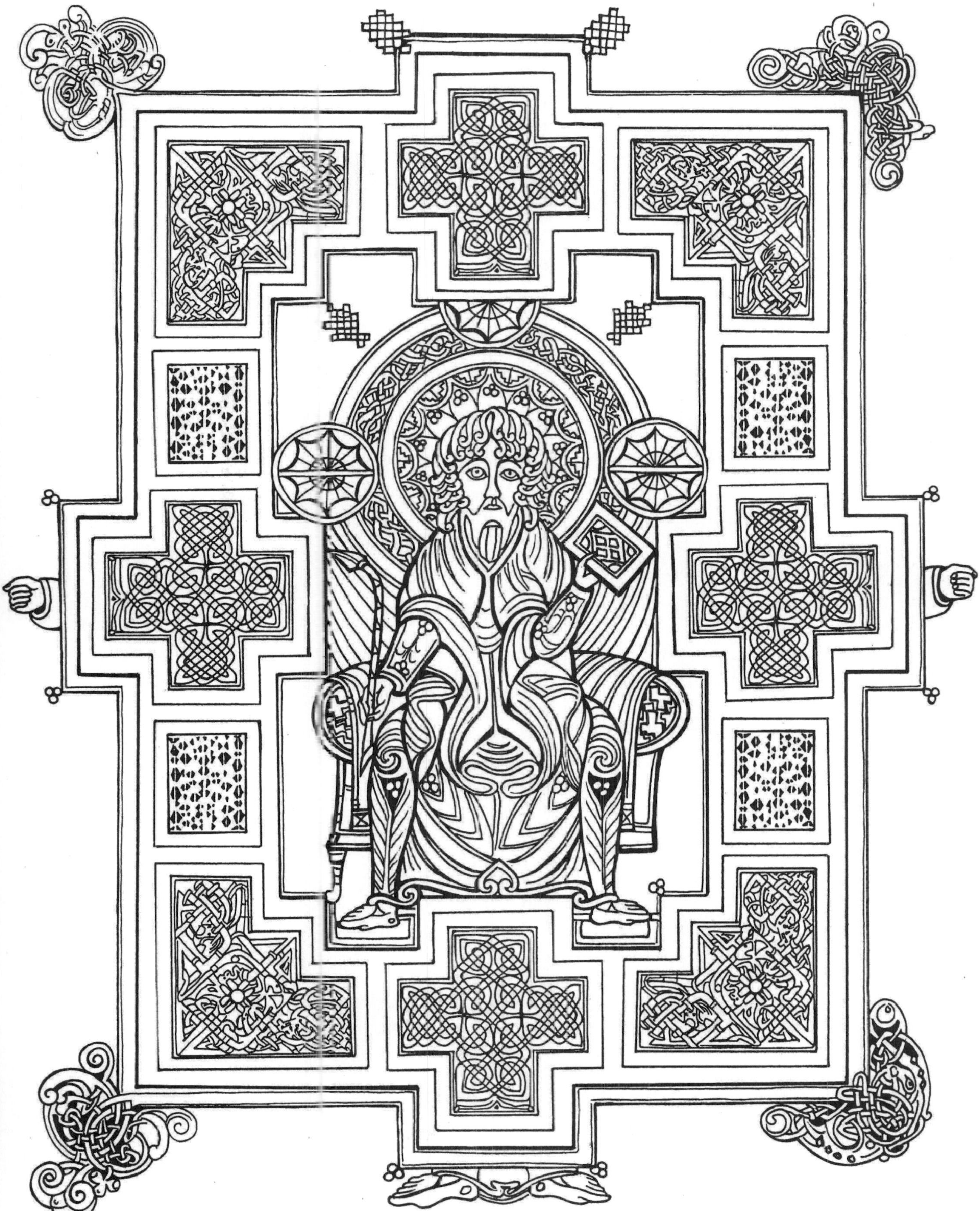

IS FÉIDIR LEIS AN LÁ IS FEARR DE DO
AM ATÁ CAITE A BHEITH AR AN LÁ IS
MEASA DE DO THODHCHAÍ

May the best of your yesterdays be the worst of your tomorrows

CAPALL na
HOÍBRE AN BÍA

Food is what will keep you going

THVILLFEADH ÉINNE
AIRGEAD, ACH IS FEAR GASTA
A CHOIMÉADFADH É

Anyone can earn money, but it is a clever man
who can keep it

A RÁ BEAG ACH DEIR SÉ GO MAITH

Say little but say it well

There's no place like home

NÍL AON TINTEÁN MAR DO THINTEÁN FÉIN

Níor bhris focal maith fiacail riamh

A good word never broke a tooth!

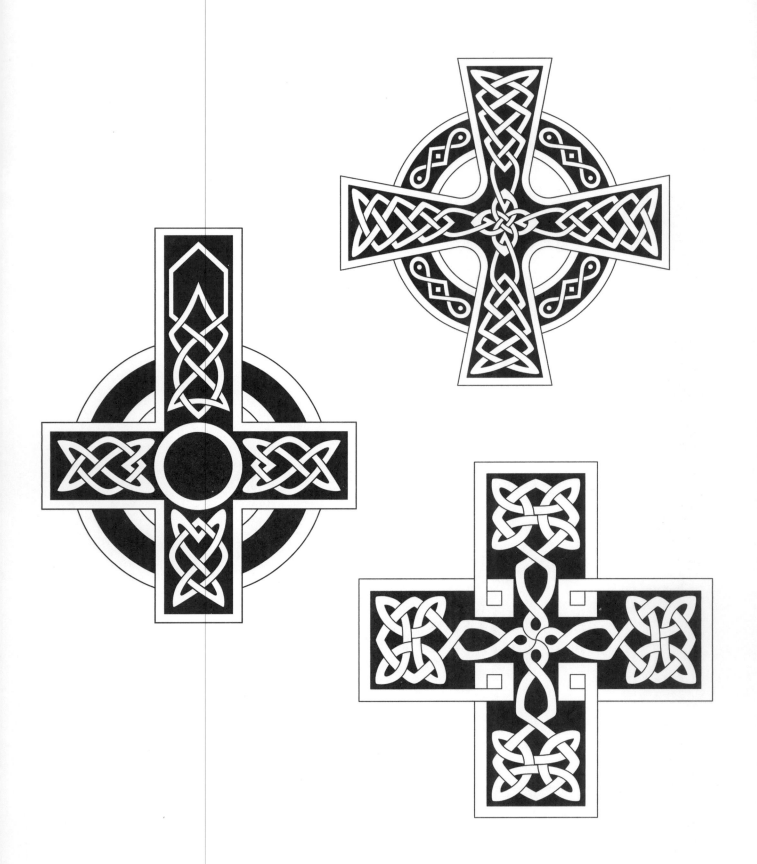

CELTIC CROSSES

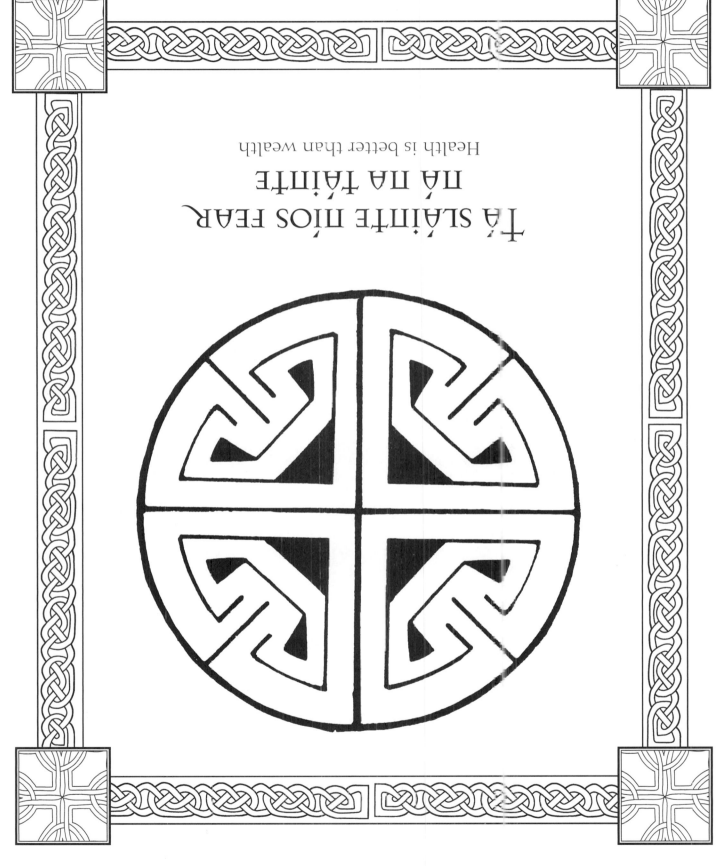

Tá sláinte níos fearr ná na táinte

Health is better than wealth

Celtic Designs

Nuair is gann é an bia is ea is fial e a roinnt

If there is not much food it is generous to share it

Ní huasal ná íseal, ach thuas seal is thíos seal

Noble or lowly, everyone has ups and downs

Knots and Spirals

THE CELTS WERE MASTERS of Insular Art, embedding their beliefs within distinctive symmetrical patterns rather than in the written word, thus leaving all meaning open to imagination and interpretation. So we wonder, do the interlace designs of flowing, never-ending ribbon-like spirals represent the gentle ebb and flow of nature as season follows season, or perhaps the continuity of being from the physical world to the immortal? And are the complicated knots, favored by the Celts so prevalently, symbolic of a universal infinity or of hope for a pure and enduring love? What we are certain of is that these striking graphics remain potent today and will do so for centuries to come.

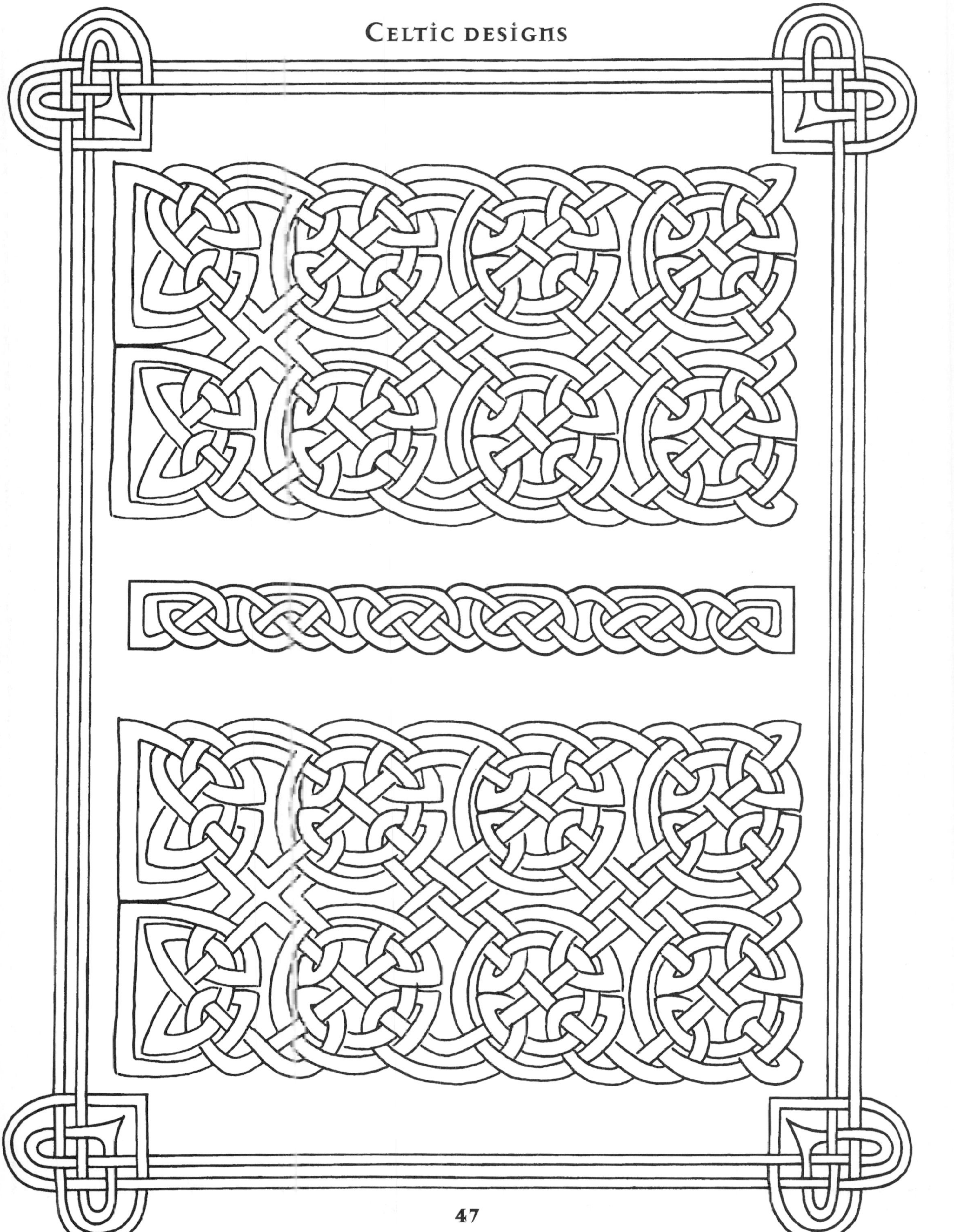

AN RUD A LÍONAS AN tSÚIL LÍONANN SÉ AN CROÍ

What fills the eye fills the heart

FAOÍ FOSCADH AR A CHÉILE, MAIREACHTÁIL LE DAOINE

Under the shelter of each other, people live better

AN RUD IS ANNAMH IS
IONTACH

What's seldom is wonderful

Is maith an scéalaí an aimsir.
Time is a great storyteller

Níl saoí gan locht

We have all got our faults

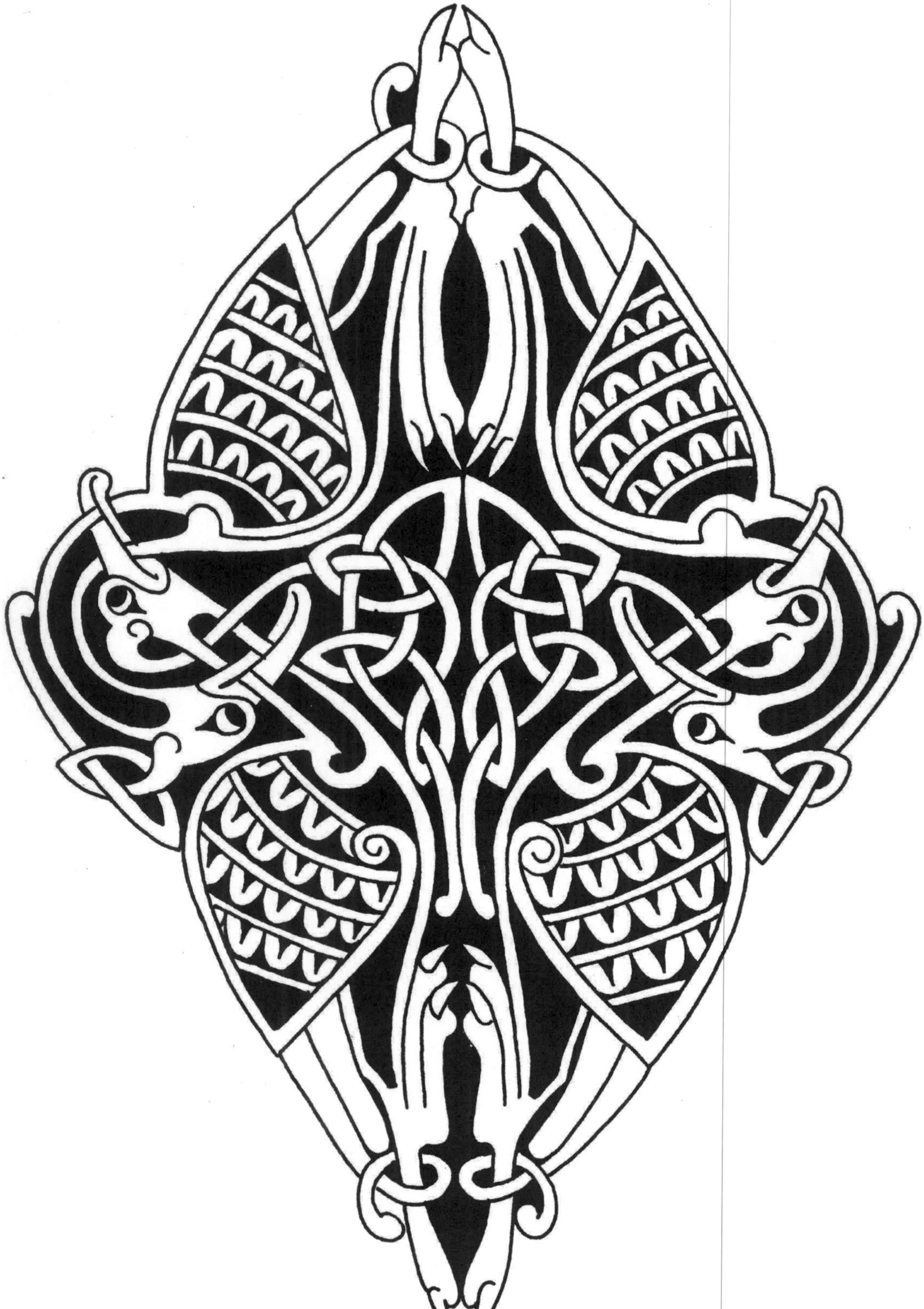

GlÓRAÍONN BEIRT BÓTHAR

Two people shorten the road

Things may not be as they seem

Ní mar a síltear a bítear

FÉASTA ANOCHT AGUS BÉIDH AMÁRACH GORTA

Feast tonight and you will famine tomorrow

KNOTS AND SPIRALS

MOLL AN ÓIGE AGUS TIOCFAIDH SÍ

Praise youth and youth will respond

Zoomorphic Imagery

ANIMAL IMAGERY AND symbolism began to appear in Celtic design at the beginning of the 9th century, an artistic development that coincided with the invasion and colonisation of parts of Eire by Viking marauders. The Norse influence meant that Interlace designs began to incorporate mythical creatures, each bestowed with a spiritual power or attributed with emotion. Religious protocol dictated that animals had to be recreated in a reductive or exaggerated form, with only the heads or tails barely recognisable as the earthly species they represented. Look for zoomorphism in the illustrations of the iconic Book of Kells, where the Disciples Matthew, Mark, Luke and John are characterised as beasts.

AN RUD NACH FÍU É A LORG, NÍ FÍU Í A FHÁIL

What is not worth seeking, is not worth finding

CAITHFIDH SÉ NACH BHFUIL
LÁIDIR, A BHEITH CLISTE

He who is not strong must be clever.

ZOOMORPHIC IMAGERY

MÁ TÚ AG LORG CARA GAN LOCHT,
BÉIDH TÚ GAN CARA GO DEO

If you are looking for a friend without fault,
you will be without a friend forever.

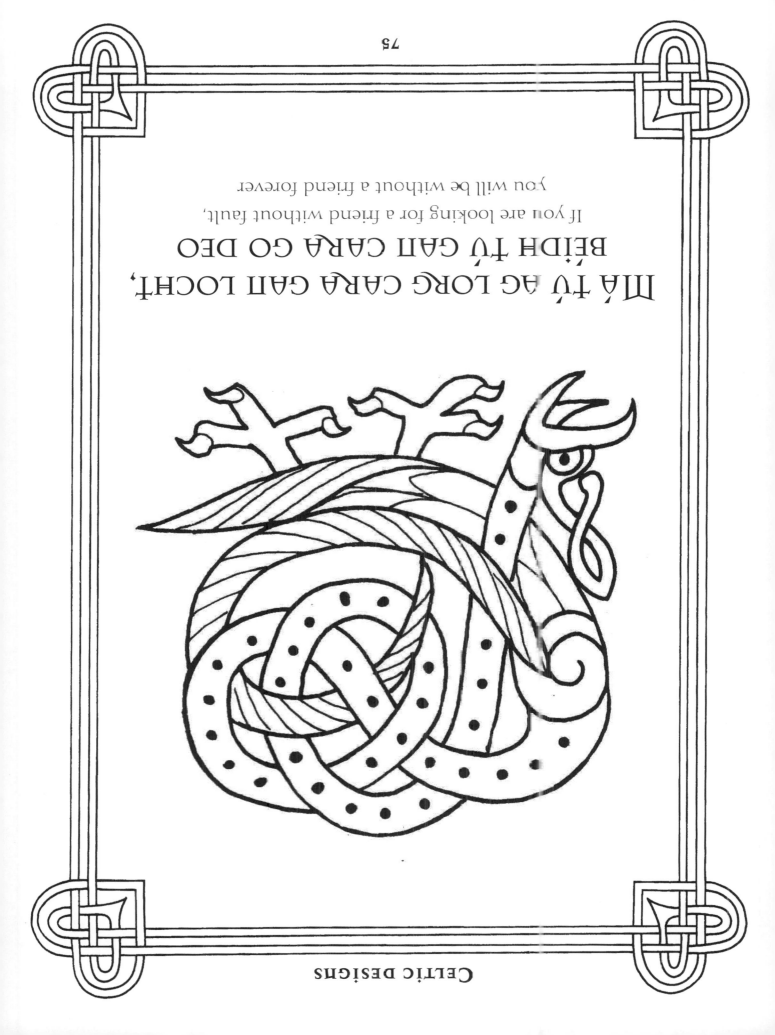

AM FEAR, IS FHAIDE CHAIDH
BHO'N BHAILE, CHUAL E'N
CEÒL BU MHILSE LEIS NUAIR
THILL E DHACHAIDH

The further away you travel away,
the sweeter it is to return home

ZOOMORPHIC IMAGERY

Beatha duine a thoil.

Everyone to his own tastes

ZOOMORPHIC IMAGERY

COÍTHEAD FEARG
FHEAR NA FÓIGHDE

Beware of the anger of a patient man

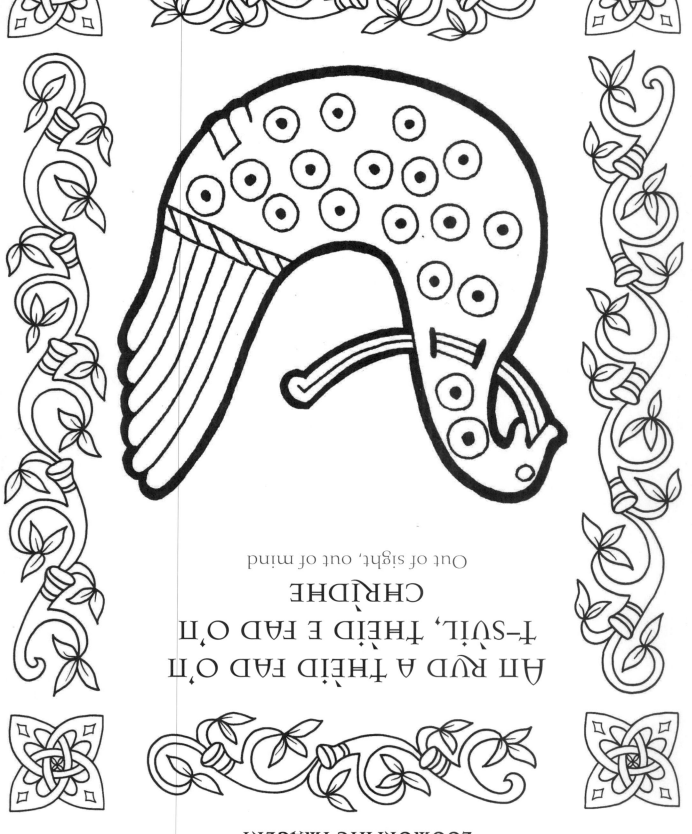

AN RUD A THÉID FAD O'N
t-SÚIL, THÉID E FAD O'N
CHRÍDHE

Out of sight, out of mind

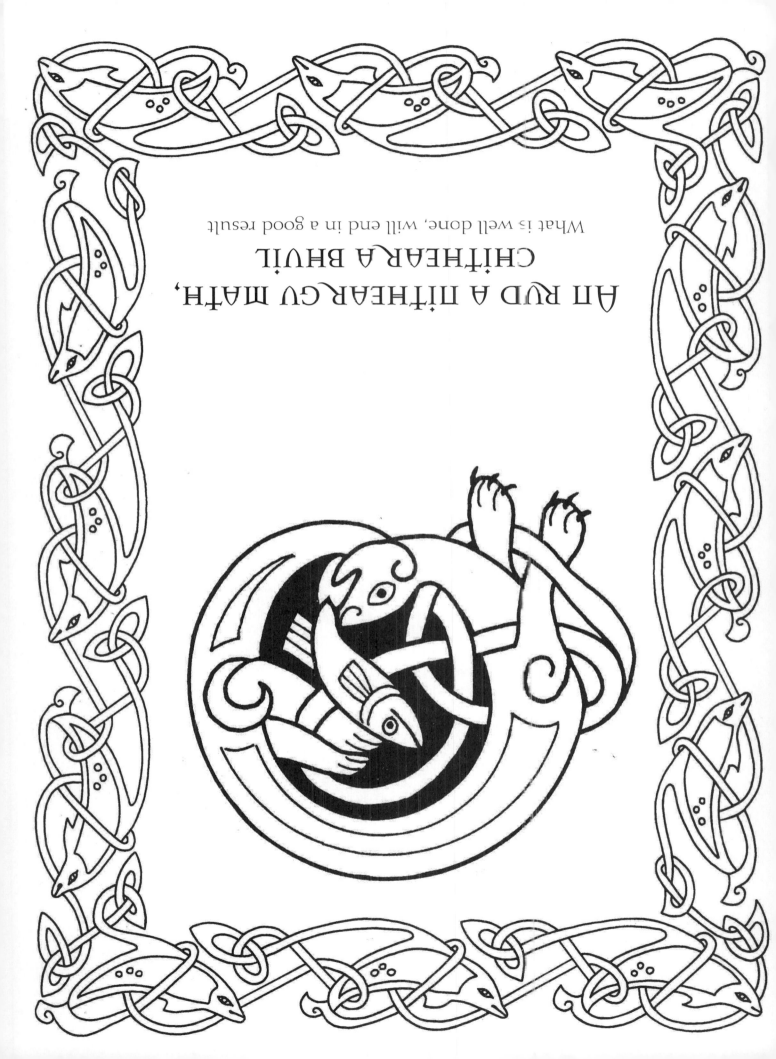

AN RUD A DITHEAR GU MATH,
CHITHEAR A BHUIL.

What is well done, will end in a good result

AN RUD NACH GABH LEASACHADH, 'S FHEUDAR CUR SUAS LEIS

What cannot be cured must be endured

He who is silent is stronger

LAIDRE

ADH AN MÉOS

TÁ SÉ ATÁ

BUÍNÍDH URRAM
DO'N AOÍS

Honor belongs to old age

ZOOMORPHIC IMAGERY

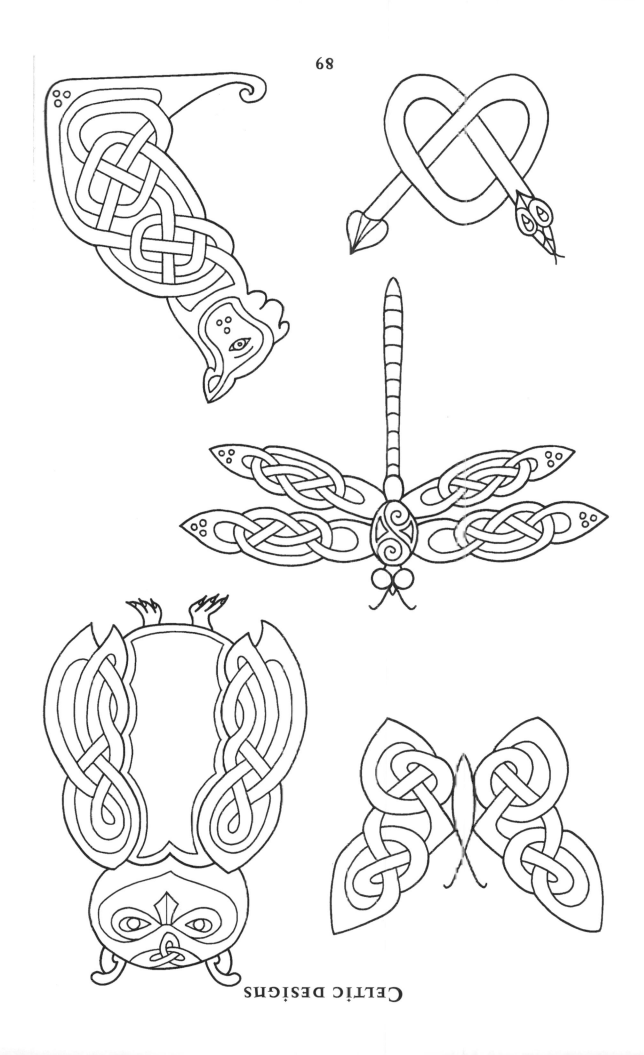

ZOOMORPHIC IMAGERY

An ní 's an teid dàil theid dearmaid

What is delayed will never be done

BHEIR DUINE BEATH' AIR
ÉIGIN, ACH CHA TOIR E
RATH AIR ÉIGIN

A man may force his livelihood,
but he cannot force his fortune

ZOOMORPHIC IMAGERY

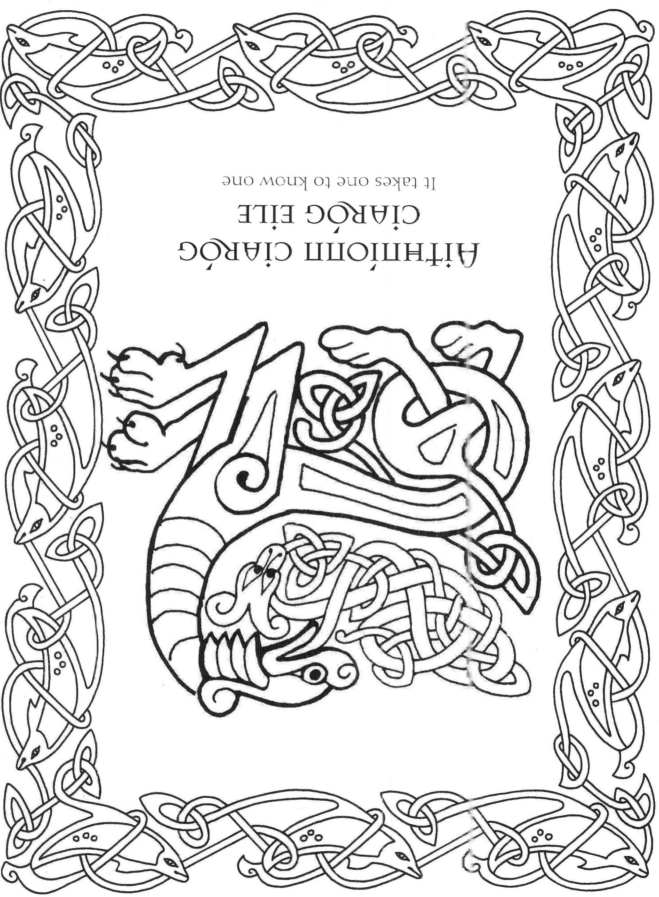

AithríoNN ciaróg ciaróg eile

It takes one to know one

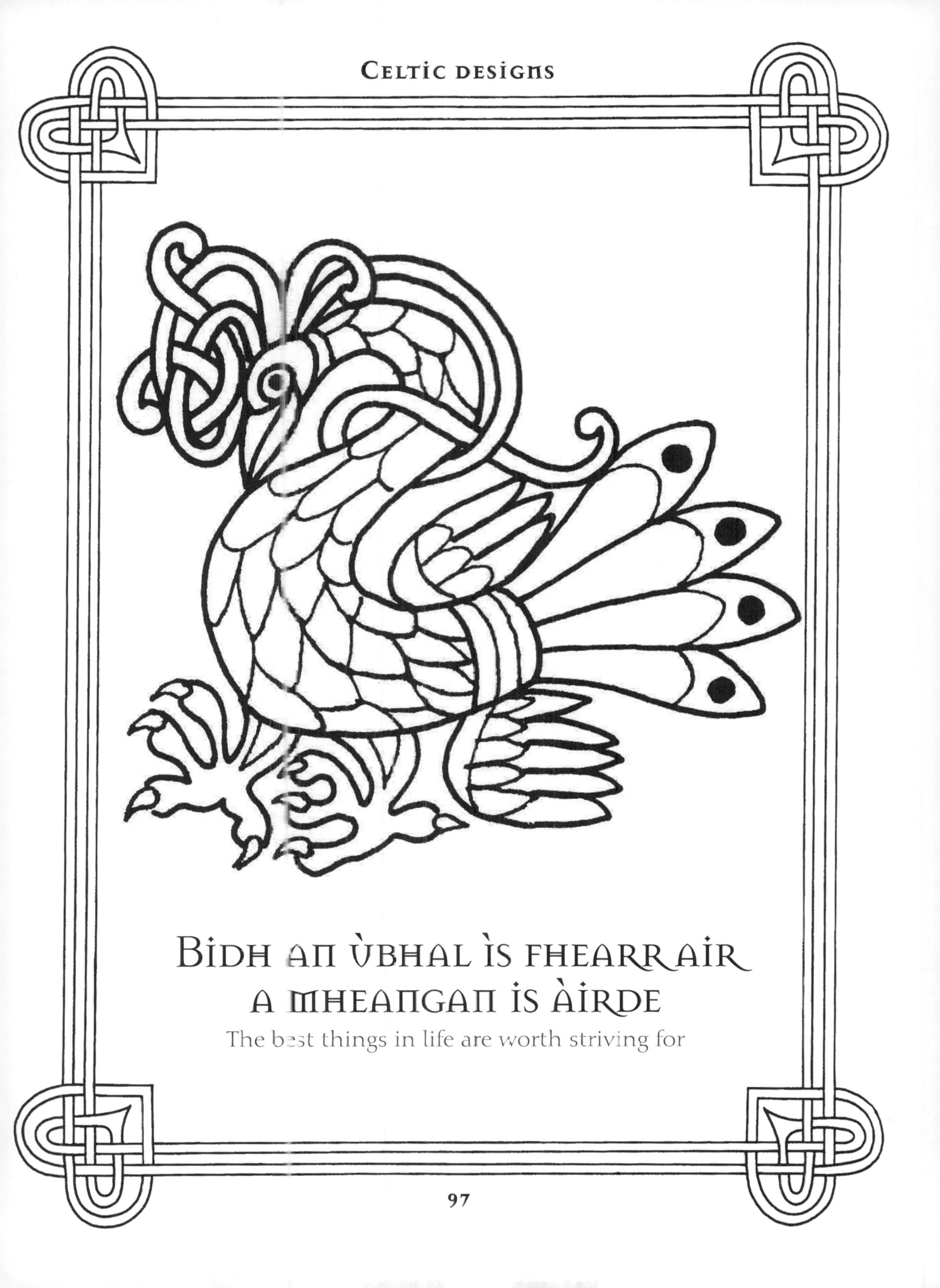

BIDH AN ÙBHAL IS FHEARRAIR
A MHEANGAN IS ÀIRDE
The best things in life are worth striving for

CHA D'THUG GAOL LUATH,
NACH D'THUG FUATH CLIS

Quick to love, quick to hate

ZOOMORPHIC IMAGERY

ZOOMORPHIC IMAGERY

CHA'N FHEUM AN TI A
SHEALBHAICHEAS AN TORADH
AM BLÀTH A MHILLEADH

Good things come to those who wait

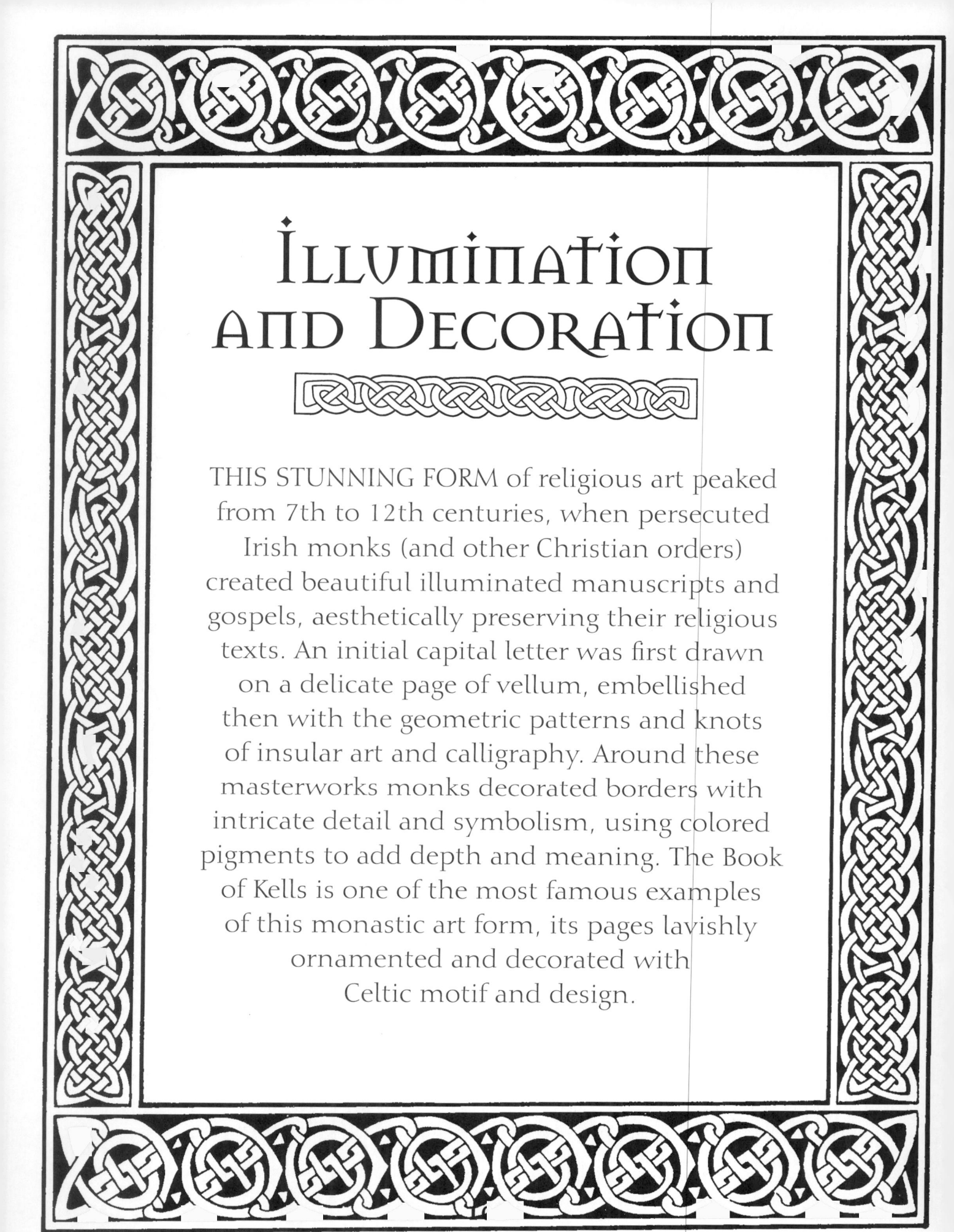

İLLVMİNATİON AND DECORATION

THIS STUNNING FORM of religious art peaked
from 7th to 12th centuries, when persecuted
Irish monks (and other Christian orders)
created beautiful illuminated manuscripts and
gospels, aesthetically preserving their religious
texts. An initial capital letter was first drawn
on a delicate page of vellum, embellished
then with the geometric patterns and knots
of insular art and calligraphy. Around these
masterworks monks decorated borders with
intricate detail and symbolism, using colored
pigments to add depth and meaning. The Book
of Kells is one of the most famous examples
of this monastic art form, its pages lavishly
ornamented and decorated with
Celtic motif and design.

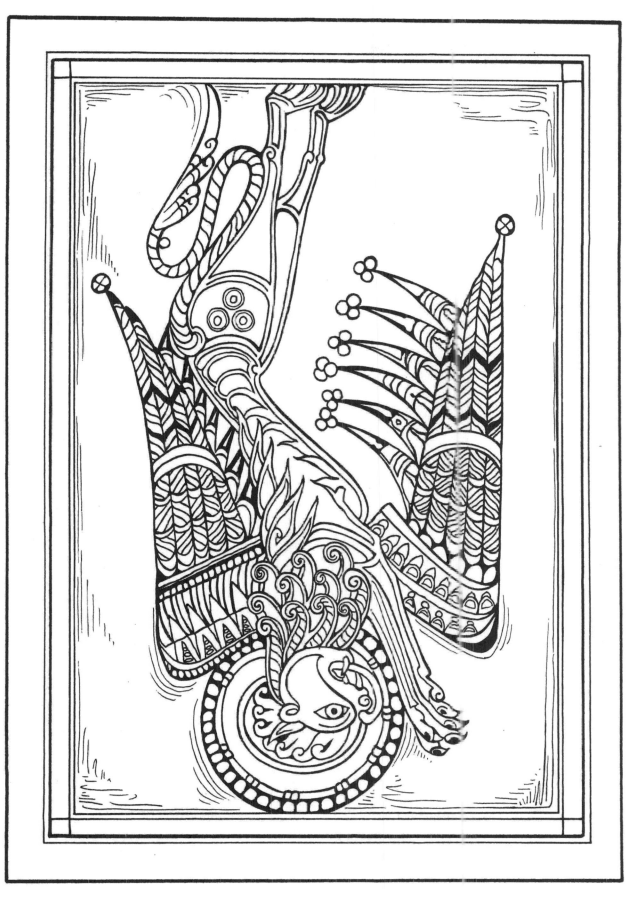

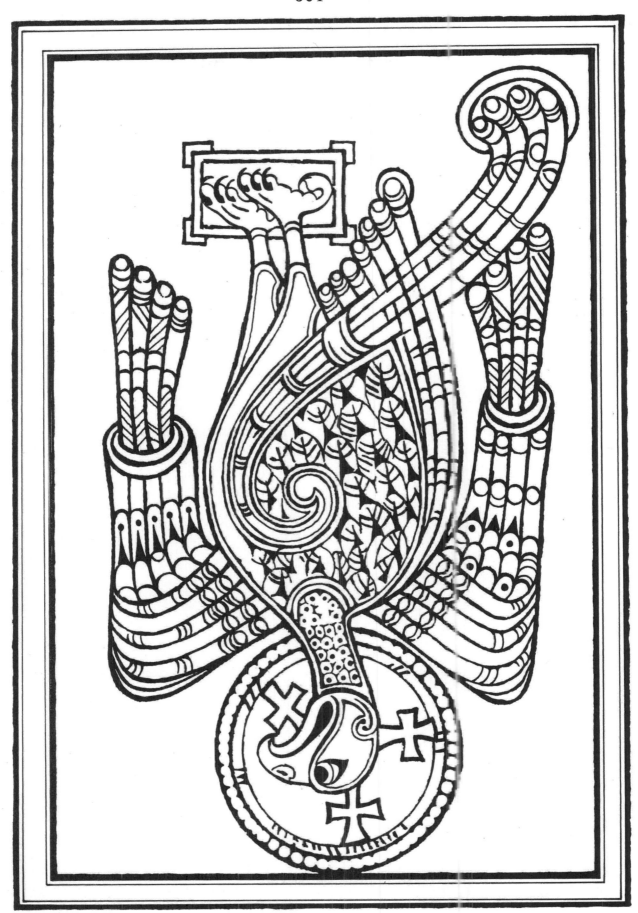

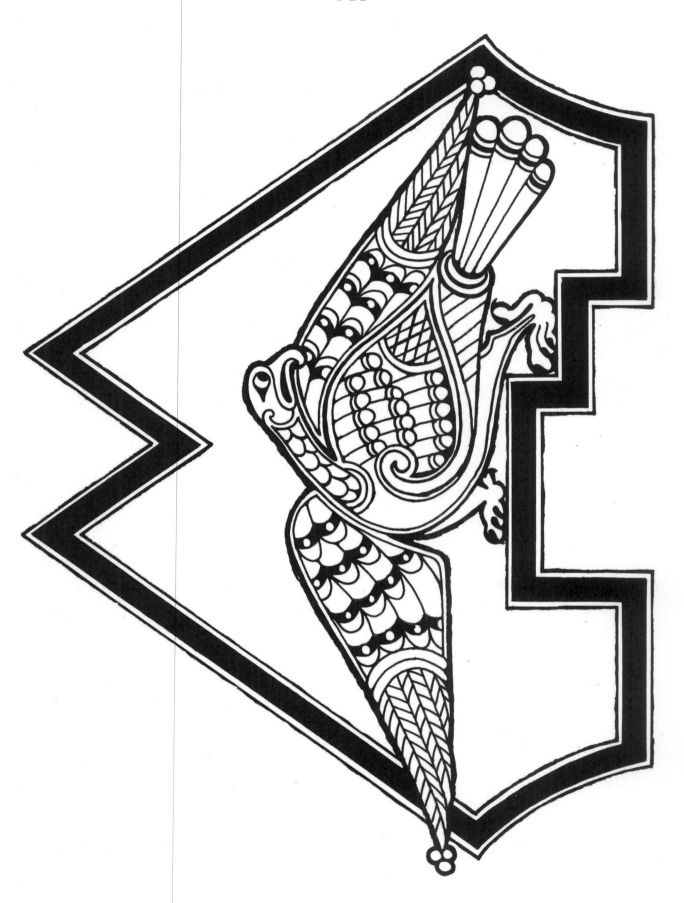

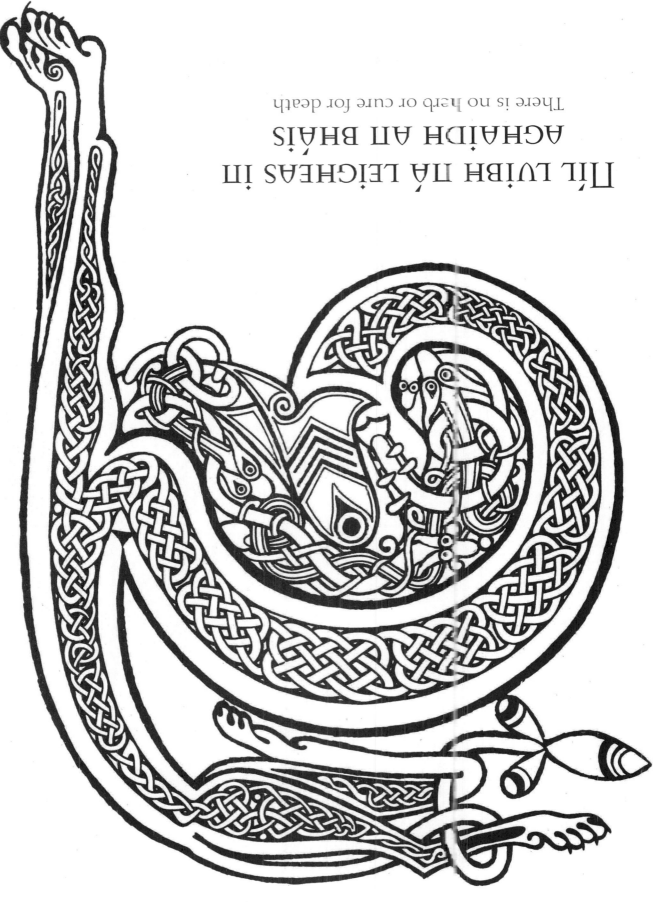

Níl luibh ná leigheas in
aghaidh an bháis

There is no herb or cure for death

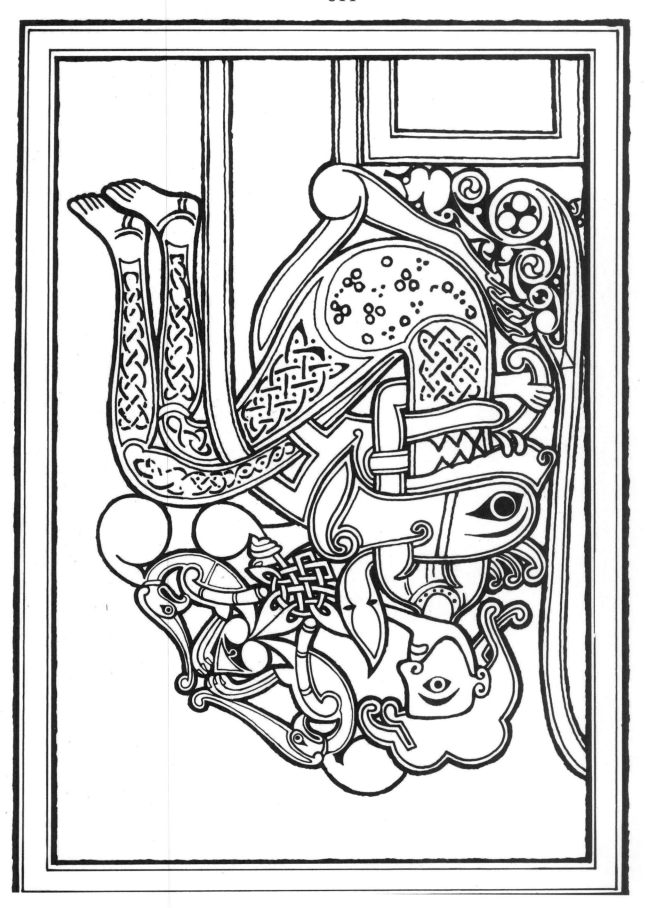

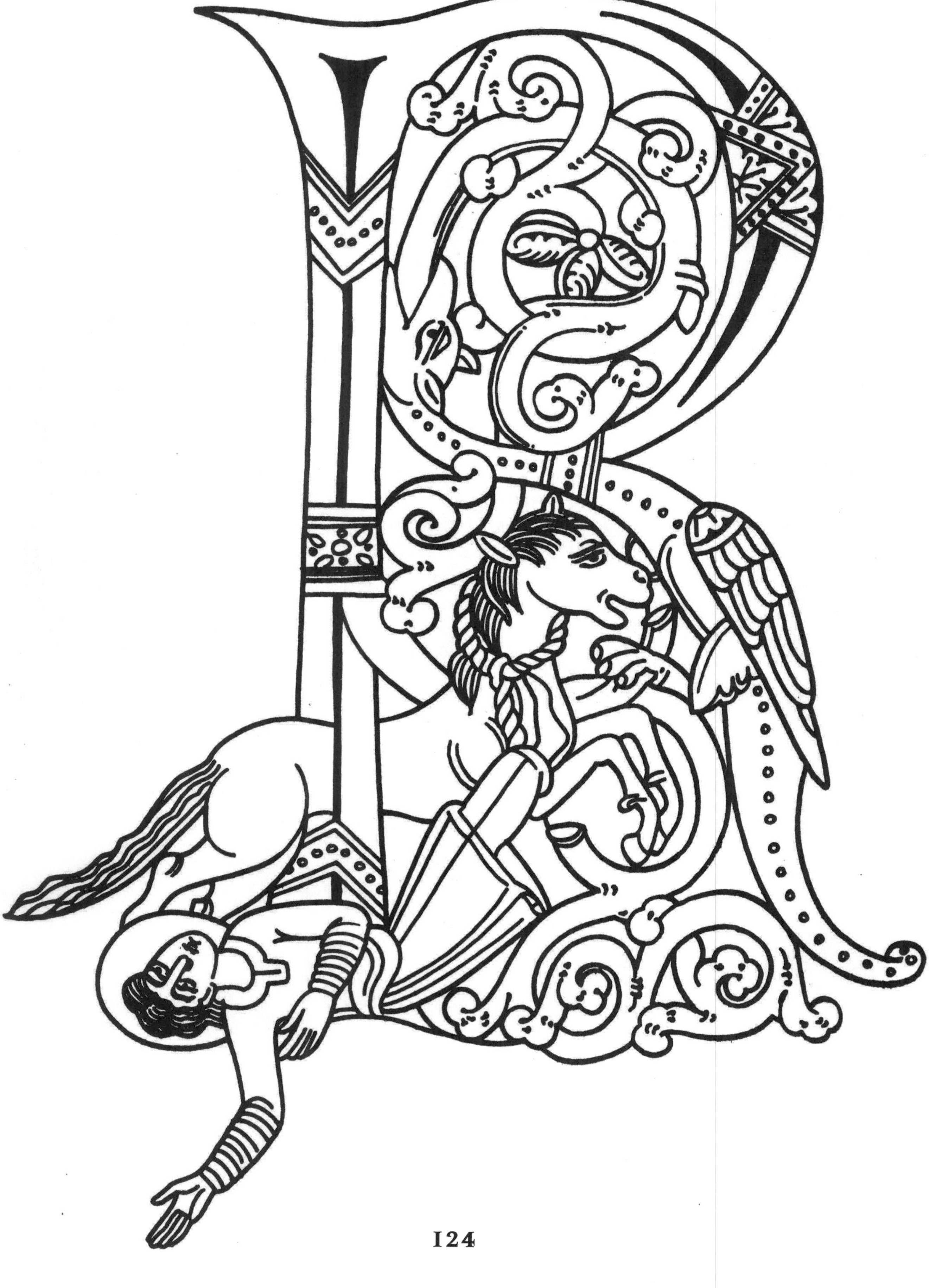

TÍR GAN TEANGA TÍR
GAN ANAM

A country without a language is a country
without a soul